The Highland Games

Written by Jill Atkins

Illustrated by Shelagh McNicholas

In the summer Alison went to stay
with her gran and grandad in
Scotland. A boy called Jamie lived
next door to them. One day Alison
and Grandad were going to the
Highland Games.
'We will see Jamie at the games,'
said Alison. 'He's doing a
Scottish dance.'

2

When they got to the Highland Games
Alison said to Grandad, 'Can I go and
look for Jamie?'
'Yes,' said Grandad.

Alison soon saw
Jamie. He was
with a tall girl
with very long
hair.

Alison said to Jamie, 'You look good
in your kilt. I wish I had one.'
Then Alison smiled at the girl but the
girl didn't smile back. She just turned
and walked away.

'Who was that?' asked Alison.

'That's Laura,' said Jamie. 'I dance
with her.'

'She's not very nice,' said Alison.

'No,' said Jamie. 'I don't like dancing
with her but I'm the only one who is
as tall as she is.'

Just then, the Highland Games began. Alison and Jamie saw lots of strong men who threw things and pushed and pulled things.
Then Alison and Jamie saw Laura again. She was following them.

Next Alison and Jamie saw a big man throwing a hammer.

'I can do that,' said Jamie, and he began to turn and turn until he fell over.

Then Laura came over and said to Jamie, 'You're so silly.'

Alison wished Laura would go away
but she went on following them.
Next Alison and Jamie went to see
the sword dance.
'I can do that,' said Alison, and she
began to dance and dance until she
fell over.
Then Laura came over and said to her,
'You're so silly.'

'Come on,' said Jamie quietly.
'Let's get away from Laura.'
Alison and Jamie ran across the field
to see the men tossing the caber.
'Look! There's Grandad,'
shouted Alison.

Grandad's friend
was tossing the
caber.
'He's the very best,'
said Grandad.

Grandad's friend asked Alison if she
would like to try to toss the caber.
'It's too heavy,' laughed Alison.
'It's as big as a tree!'

'You're not very strong are you?' said
Laura. 'I'm much stronger than you.'
'No, you're not!' said Alison.
'Yes, I am,' said Laura. 'Come with me.
I'll show you.'
So Alison and Jamie followed Laura
across the field.

She led them over to some children who
were going to have a tug of war.
'Come on, Alison,' said Jamie.
'We'll go to this end.'

So Alison and Jamie went to one end
of the rope and Laura went to the other.

'One, two, three, pull!' the teacher
shouted, and everyone began to pull
as hard as they could.

Suddenly they all fell over.
Alison and Jamie laughed.

But then Laura called out, 'I've hurt
my ankle. I can't walk on it.'
Jamie's teacher helped Laura over to
a chair.
'Oh Laura,' said her teacher. 'Now
you can't dance.'

'Alison, will you dance with me?'
asked Jamie.
'If you show me what to do,'
said Alison, and off they went.

At first Alison was not very good
but soon she was dancing very well.

When the dance was over, Jamie's
teacher said, 'Let's say a big thank you
to Alison for helping us out.'
Then Laura came up to Alison and said,
'You danced well for your first time.
One day you could be as good as me.'